THE MICROWAVE
Shakespeare

Other titles in the series

ROMEO
&
JULIET

Barbara Catchpole
&
Stephen Rickard

Illustrated by Anna Steinberg

Ransom

Romeo & Juliet
Published by Ransom Publishing Ltd.
Unit 7, Brocklands Farm, West Meon, Hampshire GU32 1JN, UK
www.ransom.co.uk

ISBN   978 178591 339 6
First published in 2019

CONTENTS

WHERE

Verona, a small city in the north of Italy.

Verona

ITALY

WHEN

The events in the play take place sometime between about 1300 and 1400 (600 – 700 years ago).

This is the 'Renaissance' period.

The play itself was written in about 1595.

WHO

The Montague family

Benvolio – a Montague nobleman.
He is serious and sensitive

Romeo – cousin to Benvolio.
A romantic soul

Mercutio – friend of Romeo, friend of the
Montague family. Brash, bold and witty

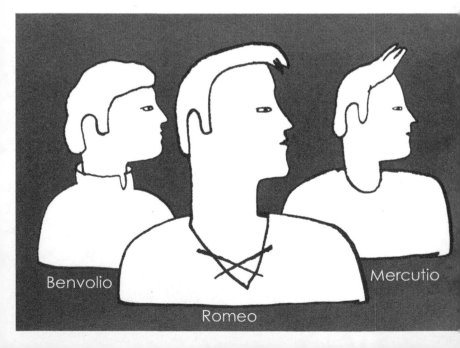

Benvolio

Romeo

Mercutio

The Capulet Family

Lord Capulet – head of the Capulet family. Strict

Lady Capulet – his wife

Juliet – their daughter. She is nearly fourteen

Tybalt – a Capulet nobleman. Juliet's cousin. He is good with a sword, proud and fashionable. Keen to protect the Capulet name

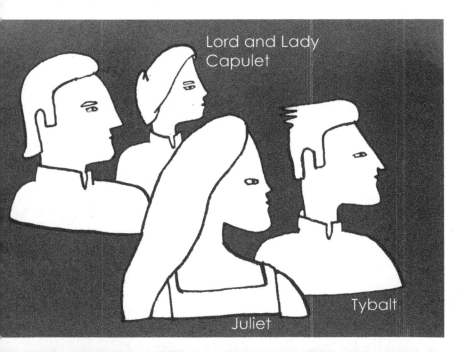

Lord and Lady Capulet

Juliet

Tybalt

Prince Escales – Prince of Verona

Paris – a nobleman, friend of Prince Escales and friend of the Capulets

Friar Laurence – a clever and devout man. He is full of good intentions

Friar John – Friar Laurence's messenger

Balthasar – Romeo's servant

The Nurse – Juliet's nurse

Sampson – a Capulet servant

Peter – a Capulet servant

Helpful Note

All the spoken words in this book that are in italics, *'like this'*, are actual words taken from Shakespeare's play. They are spoken by one of the actors in the play.

The Globe Theatre. Above is a reconstruction of the original Globe Theatre, which is in London. Below is a cross-section of the original theatre, which was built in 1599.

Shakespeare's plays were performed at this theatre. When you read this book, just imagine standing in the crowd, in front of this stage, watching the play.

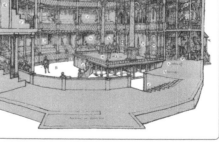

ONE

Sampson, a servant of the Capulet family, is trying to start a street fight with some servants of the Montague family. (To put it nicely, the Capulets and the Montagues do not get on!)

Samson bites his thumb at the Montagues, which in Italy is a way of showing contempt for someone. It's a big insult – and it starts a fight!

Benvolio, a Montague nobleman and an all-round nice guy, tries to part the brawling servants. He's doing his best to keep the peace.

Then, unluckily, **Tybalt Capulet** comes

swaggering down the street and
immediately draws his expensive sword.

Tybalt likes nothing better than a sword
fight. He practises all the time. And he hates
the Montagues with a dark, black rage.

Very quickly there are servants and
noblemen brawling everywhere – even old

Lord Capulet and Lord Montague. The street is full of shouting men and blood is flowing.

Prince Escales of Verona stands watching the messy fight. This is *his* town – and yet he can't control it! This is the third time this has happened. The prince is livid! He has to stop it.

'Listen up, you lot! Stop this now!' he shouts.

Then he tells them straight: if this happens again, there will be executions:

'*Once more, on pain of death, all men depart.*'

Later that day, in another part of Verona, **Romeo Montague** is out walking.

He is feeling depressed and hasn't been able to sleep. He is in love with a girl named Rosaline, but she's told him she doesn't want him. In fact, she isn't planning on going with any boys at all. So that all seems pretty final.

Romeo strolls along the street with his cousin Benvolio, chatting and looking sadly at the mess left from the street fight earlier.

Benvolio suggests a simple solution to Romeo's problem: there are plenty of girls around – just pick another one!

'*Examine other beauties*,' he says to Romeo. But Romeo says he could never love another. He will love Rosaline forever …

Meanwhile, at the Capulets' house, another nobleman, **Count Paris** (friend of Prince Escales), has decided which girl he wants to marry. It is thirteen-year-old **Juliet**, daughter of **Lord Capulet**.

So Paris asks Lord Capulet if he can marry her. Lord Capulet isn't keen – Juliet is his only child, she isn't even fourteen and (in those days) marriage usually meant babies straight away. And Lord Capulet thinks Juliet is still too young for all that.

So Lord Capulet tells Paris that he should wait two years – until Juliet is at least fifteen.

But he does invite Paris to a ball (read: big party!) that he is holding. (Parties make everything better!)

Lord Capulet then sends a servant out with invitations to all the nobility of Verona (except for the horrid Montagues, of course, who obviously aren't invited).

Bad luck, though! The servant who is sent out with the party invitations can't read.

But it turns out OK (kind of) – the servant meets Romeo and Benvolio by chance in the street. Romeo is still whining to Benvolio about Rosaline.

The two men help the servant out and read the invitations for him.

Then Benvolio has a great idea: he and Romeo could gate-crash the Capulet ball! (Don't forget – Romeo and Benvolio are Montagues.) Romeo could meet some beautiful girls at the party, to help him get over this Rosaline.

Juliet's mother, **Lady Capulet**, is talking to Juliet about Count Paris' offer of marriage.

'*The valiant Paris seeks you for his love*,' she says.

Juliet agrees that she'll at least have a look at this Paris guy at the party.

After Benvolio's brainwave, the Montague family decide that they are *all* going to go to Lord Capulet's ball, invitation or no invitation.

(Luckily it's going to be a masked ball, so they should be able to attend without being recognised.)

Romeo still thinks going is a really bad idea. He tells them they'll have to drag him there.

Mercutio, a Montague family friend and, frankly, a bit of a lad, urges them on.

'So Romeo had a bad dream,' says Mercutio. 'Well,' he says, 'so did I.'

He had dreamed of Queen Mab, Queen of the Fairies, who causes dreams – often with tragic results for the dreamer. She even causes maids to become pregnant.

They have to tell Mercutio (always reckless and loud) to be quiet.

'*Peace, peace, Mercutio, peace!*
Thou talk'st of nothing,' says Romeo.

'True,' says Mercutio. 'Dreams come to nothing. You can dream, but it will all turn to dust!'

(Cheerful stuff.)

Romeo is still feeling depressed (no wonder!) and thinks nothing good can come from the evening.

But he agrees to go ...

The Capulet ball is in full swing. The young people are dancing and the old people are remembering their pasts. Just like parties today.

Then, two things happen at the same time: Romeo sees Juliet, and Tybalt sees Romeo.

Instantly, on seeing Juliet, Romeo falls head-over-heels in love with her. He is straight over there, chatting to Juliet and

trying to steal a kiss. All thoughts of Rosaline have swiftly vanished from his good-looking head.

As for Tybalt, as soon as he sees Romeo (who is a Montague, remember), he falls into a black rage.

' 'Tis he, that villain Romeo,' says Tybalt. He immediately tells his uncle, Lord Capulet, that the Montagues have crashed the party. Tybalt says he will kill Romeo, here and now, but Lord Capulet says, 'No.'

'Be quiet, or … For shame! I'll make you quiet,' he tells Tybalt. (Lord Capulet doesn't want blood spilled at his party: it makes a terrible mess, and anyway all that blood makes you look like a bad host.)

So Tybalt is forced to swallow his anger – but he swears that he will get even with Romeo.

After the ball, Romeo realises he must see Juliet again. Immediately. This is his only chance! (In those days, young unmarried girls were shut away for most of the time.)

He gives Mercutio and poor Benvolio the slip and sneaks into the Capulet's orchard (basically, their back garden).

There Romeo sees Juliet standing on the balcony of her room.

'*But, soft! what light through yonder window breaks?*

It is the east, and Juliet is the sun.

Arise, fair sun, and kill the envious moon,' he says.

Obviously, he's got it bad.

Juliet, too, had been too excited to sleep after the ball. Hot from tossing and turning, she'd gone out onto her balcony to cool down.

'*O Romeo, Romeo! wherefore art thou Romeo?*' she says. She knows he's a Montague – a sworn enemy of the Capulets. 'But,' she says, '*What's in a name? that which we call a rose*

By any other name would smell as sweet.'
(He may be a Montague, but, 'What does his name matter? He is perfection!')

She's got it bad, too.

Romeo's heart thuds as he hears Juliet's words. His love loves him in return!

He steps out into the light. Juliet is startled to see him – and scared, because if her family finds him there, they will kill him.

Cue the famous balcony scene. In the moonlight, they frantically declare their love for each other and exchange their vows. They decide they must get married quickly – before the adults can stop them! Then the whole of Verona will just have to deal with it!

Juliet is practical: Romeo must get everything organised straight away. She will send a messenger to him tomorrow to obtain all the details – when and where they will marry.

It is almost dawn, the start of another swelteringly hot day in Verona. Romeo, full of excitement and love, rushes off to find a priest to arrange the wedding. He finds **Friar Laurence**, gathering herbs to make medicine.

Friar Laurence is a clever and devout man. At first he is shocked, thinking that Romeo has spent the night with Rosaline. But he quickly sees that Romeo has moved on to Juliet Capulet.

Suddenly, Friar Laurence has a brainwave. Like most people in Verona, he is fed up with the feuding and bloodshed between the Capulets and the Montagues. If Romeo and Juliet get married, it might unite the two families and stop all the fighting.

'*For this alliance may so happy prove,*

To turn your households' rancour [hatred] *to pure love,*' he says to Romeo.

Friar Laurence agrees to marry them at once.

Romeo rushes back into Verona to wait for Juliet's messenger.

Meanwhile, Mercutio and Benvolio are hanging out together on the street.

Mercutio is worried because Tybalt has challenged Romeo to a duel, sending the challenge to Romeo's house.

Mercutio knows that Tybalt loves nothing better than a sword fight. He practises all the time, so he is very deadly – and Romeo has been made soppy by being in love.

In other words, Romeo is in trouble!

Then Romeo joins Mercutio and Benvolio on the street. He's cheered up a bit since yesterday.

And then, Juliet's **Nurse** turns up. Juliet has sent her to get the details of the secret wedding with Romeo. The nurse has dressed up with a huge head-dress – and the servant, **Peter**, is attending her as if she were a noble lady.

Mercutio shouts out long and loud that she must be some old woman who is after Romeo!

Romeo is so embarrassed! He takes the nurse to one side, well away from Mercutio, and tells her that Juliet should go to Friar Laurence for confession that afternoon. Once there, Romeo will meet her and they will be married.

Romeo will send his servant to the nurse with a rope ladder, so that he, Romeo, can climb up to his Juliet that night, after they are safely married.

Back at the Capulets', after a lot of complaining ('Oh my poor aching bones! From now on you can take your own messages!'), the nurse tells Juliet of the plan.

'I am doing all the work now – but you will be active tonight!' she says to Juliet.

The nurse is rude, but Juliet loves her.

So that very afternoon, not twenty-four

hours after they first met, Romeo and Juliet are secretly married. Neither of them could be happier.

And yet … and yet … Friar Laurence feels the need to warn Romeo:

'These violent delights have violent ends.'

TwO

Mercutio, Benvolio and their servants are hanging out on the streets of Verona. (Do they ever do anything else?) It's so hot!

Benvolio wants to get Mercutio in off the street. He knows that if they meet the Capulets, there will be a fight.

Sure enough, they walk slap-bang into Tybalt and his Capulet gang. The two groups of young men stand and look at each other.

They all know there's going to be a fight! It's going to happen!

Then Tybalt breaks the silence and asks

for a word with Mercutio. Mercutio replies by saying it should be a word *and* a blow. In other words, he's ready for a fight.

But Tybalt doesn't want to fight Mercutio. He is looking for Romeo. He is still mad at Romeo for gate-crashing the party.

Just at that moment, Romeo walks down the street.

Good timing! *Not.*

Tybalt turns to Romeo: '*Thou art a villain!*'

Tybalt wants to have a swordfight with Romeo, there and then. Tybalt has had lessons – he will win! He hates Romeo.

Of course, Romeo backs off. He has just married Tybalt's cousin, Juliet, so he and Tybalt are now related.

Romeo only wants peace. In his mind, he is already climbing that silk ladder to Juliet.

'*Turn and draw,*' Tybalt yells to Romeo.

Wild Mercutio thinks that Tybalt is insolent – and Romeo is being a wimp. So he offers to fight Tybalt on Romeo's behalf.

'Tybalt, you rat-catcher, will you walk?'
Mercutio shouts.

Romeo frantically tries to stop them, but
sneaky Tybalt thrusts his shiny, sharp sword
under Romeo's arm and deep into Mercutio's
lungs. Immediately Tybalt is off, running
through the hot deserted streets.

Mercutio sort
of sags, muttering
to himself,
'*a scratch, a
scratch.*'

The others
think he is
pretending to be
hurt, for a laugh.
'*Courage,
man; the hurt
cannot be much,*'
says Romeo.

Then they all
see the blood seeping through his loose shirt
– so much blood!

They help him into a house, so that he does not die in the street.

As he lies there, Mercutio looks Romeo full in the face and curses the Montagues and the Capulets:

'A *plague o' both your houses! They have made worms' meat of me.*'

Then he dies.

Romeo is mad with rage and grief. He races through the streets of Verona to find the murderer.

He catches up with Tybalt and they cross swords. Tybalt is good, but Romeo is crazy – and Tybalt falls dead.

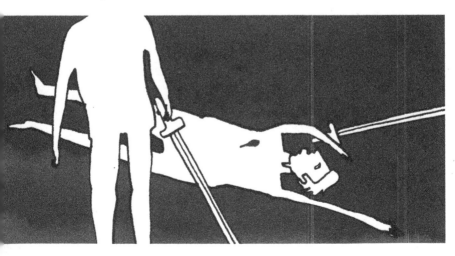

Now Romeo realises what he has done. He has broken the prince's rule about not fighting – *and* he has killed his new wife's cousin. Now he will never be accepted by the Capulets.

'*O, I am fortune's fool!*'

The crowds gather.

The prince arrives and Benvolio tells him the whole story. Benvolio says that Romeo was right to execute Tybalt for the murder of Mercutio.

The prince decides to show mercy on Romeo. Instead of executing him, he banishes him to the city of Mantua.

Romeo must leave Verona forever!

Meanwhile, Juliet knows nothing about these events. She is happily waiting for night to fall, when her Romeo will come to her.

Then the nurse rushes in and tells Juliet what has happened.

At first, Juliet is angry with Romeo. She has known Tybalt since she was tiny. They grew up together.

Then she is angry with herself for being angry with Romeo. She is his wife and she loves him. What can they do?

The nurse knows that Romeo would have run off to Friar Laurence immediately after his exile by the prince. If the prince finds Romeo there, he will be killed.

So the nurse hurries off to Friar Laurence's cell, leaving Juliet weeping and out of her mind with worry.

The nurse is sure that Friar Laurence will know what to do. He is a very wise man, after all.

Arriving at Friar Laurence's cell, the nurse hears Romeo crying. Sure enough, on entering, she sees Romeo in a right state, raging and crying and hitting himself on the chest. He's pretty upset.

She and Friar Laurence stand and watch him for a bit, before the nurse loses her patience.

'*Stand up, stand up; stand, and you be a man,*' she tells him, '*for Juliet's sake!*'

Once she has got Romeo quiet, Friar Laurence points out that it could have been a lot, lot worse. Romeo is alive. Juliet loves him. He has only to go to Mantua and wait, while his friends sort it all out. He just needs to be patient!

The friar and the nurse agree to help him to go to Juliet, so that they can have one night together before he leaves Verona – but he must leave for Mantua at dawn.

The next morning, Romeo and Juliet watch the dawn together in each others' arms. They cannot let go of each other: time is their enemy.

They watch the first fingers of light streak

the dawn. The larks start to wake and sing.

Still Romeo lingers. He says that, if Juliet chose it, he would stay and die rather than leave his new wife.

'Madam!' the nurse shouts suddenly. 'Your mother is coming!'

Juliet suddenly has a vision of the future: she sees Romeo, dead and pale, lying in a tomb.

She tells Romeo about her vision, but he makes light of it – it's just the upset of parting, he says.

He doesn't tell her that he too keeps getting this awful feeling.

Then, one last kiss – and he slides down the ladder and is gone!

Events start to darken around the lovers. Lady Capulet comes to tell Juliet that her father, Lord Capulet (always an unpredictable man), has suddenly decided to allow Count Paris to marry her.

Lord Capulet thought this would cheer everyone up after Tybalt's death. After all, there's nothing like a wedding!

Juliet is aghast! She cries out, '*I will not marry yet; and, when I do, I swear,*
   It shall be Romeo ... rather than Paris!'

Lady Capulet knows that Juliet's father will not react well to being disobeyed (and she is right!).

Lord Capulet is certainly angry at Juliet's response.

'*Hang thee, young baggage! disobedient wretch!*' he shouts.

He tells Juliet that if she refuses to go to the church, he will drag her there himself.

He calls her a '*wretched puling fool*'. ('Puling' means 'whining'; he's obviously not heard how whiny Romeo is!)

Lord Capulet carries on ranting and raving. He threatens to hit Juliet. He rages: if she does not marry, she can '*beg, starve, die in the streets'* – he will have nothing to do with her.

The nurse and Lady Capulet both try to calm him down, but he is beside himself in uncontrollable fury.

He storms out, followed by Lady Capulet, who says to Juliet, *'Talk not to me, for I'll not speak a word:*

Do as thou wilt, for I have done with thee.'

Juliet is sobbing. She asks her nurse, 'What shall I do?'

The nurse tries hard to think, but really what is to be done? Nothing! So perhaps it is better for Juliet just to accept things and marry Paris.

'Marry Paris!' says the nurse. 'Really, he is a much better man than Romeo. Anyway, Romeo cannot come back to Verona, so he's as good as dead. Marry Paris!'

For Juliet that is the final betrayal! Everyone is against her.

THREE

Friar Laurence is a clever man – everybody knows that – and at least he knows what is going on. So Juliet decides to pay him a visit. He will know what to do.

As Juliet arrives at Friar Laurence's cell, she finds Paris there, making arrangements for his wedding (to Juliet!). Awkward!

Juliet tries not to lie to Paris, but it is so difficult. Especially when Paris says that their wedding '*must be*'.

It has all been arranged between Paris

and Juliet's father. But what about her? She has had no say at all in this!

In fact, this is the first time that Juliet has even talked to Paris!

At last, Paris leaves. Juliet then talks to Friar Laurence about her grief and her desperate situation. She tells the friar that she would do anything – *anything* – rather than marry Paris.

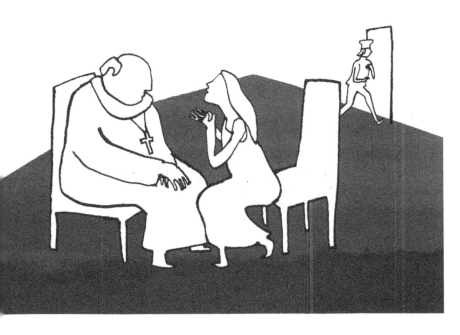

She says she would rather be in a tomb, covered in a dead man's bones, than marry him!

As it happens, that is the very thing that the clever friar is planning. He is very skilled in the use of herbs, and he tells Juliet his cunning plan.

He plans to give her a potion that will make it seem as if she were dead.

Her family, on seeing her dead, will then lay her in the family tomb with all the other dead relations.

Then the friar will send word to Romeo, who will sneak into Verona and collect her, just as the drug is wearing off and she is waking up.

Then they will both go and live in Mantua. All sorted; job done.

Brave Juliet is up for it.

'*Give me, give me!*' she responds, as Friar Laurence holds up the potion that will make her appear dead.

What could possibly go wrong?

Juliet goes home and apologises sweetly to her father. She tells him that she has spoken with Friar Laurence and he has taught her how to behave. She had been wrong and now she sees the error of her ways.

She tells her parents that she wants to go to bed early – to sort out her clothes for tomorrow and to pray.

So now, upstairs in her room, Juliet is alone with the little bottle of potion that Friar Laurence gave her.

She is terrified. Her heart is thumping in her chest. What if Friar Laurence is just poisoning her to hush things up?

What if she wakes up earlier than expected – surrounded by bones and decay? (After all, Tybalt has only just been put in the family tomb.)

What if she goes mad and dashes her own brains out with a bone?

What if it doesn't work? What then?

Juliet puts her dagger beside her. If the drugs don't work, she decides she will plunge the dagger into her breast.

With a final, '*Romeo, I come! this do I drink to thee,*' she takes a deep breath and gulps the liquid down.

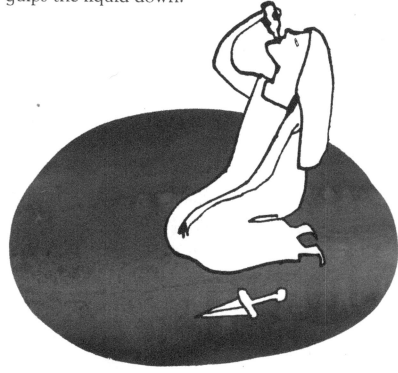

Her heart slows down. She is barely breathing.

The next morning, Paris comes to the house early.

When the nurse goes to wake Juliet, she finds her lying, it seems, quite dead.

Then there is a commotion! Everybody is weeping and wailing and screaming and crying!

They are all sorry now!

And, just as in Juliet and Friar Laurence's cunning plan, they lay Juliet to rest in the family tomb.

The wedding has turned into a funeral.

FOUR

The next part of the plan is for Friar Laurence to send a message to Romeo. The message tells Romeo that Juliet isn't really dead – and that Romeo must to come to rescue her from the tomb.

Friar Laurence's messenger, **Friar John**, is sent to deliver the message to Romeo. He's desperate to get his message delivered, but he has a problem: they won't let him enter the city of Mantua, because they are afraid that he might have the plague.

Meanwhile, Romeo's servant, **Balthasar**, who doesn't know about Friar Laurence's

plan, has had no trouble in reaching Romeo.
He made the ride to Mantua in record time
and entered the city without any problem.

In Mantua, Romeo has had a dream. He
dreamt he was lying dead and Juliet revived
him with a kiss. Now Romeo is feeling
anxious – it was such a spooky dream!
   Romeo asks Balthasar if everyone is OK.
'*News from Verona!* ...
   How fares my Juliet? that I ask again;
   For nothing can be ill, if she be well.'
Balthasar swallows hard. This is awful.

So he tells Romeo of Juliet's death.

Not surprisingly, Romeo is upset.

Actually he's heartbroken, crazy with grief. He can't believe it! It just can't be!

He must go back to Verona – there must be some mistake! Why hasn't Friar Laurence written to him?

So Romeo rides hard back to Verona, urging his horse on.

But then he has a thought – Juliet might really be dead. Then Romeo would not want to live. He decides he will get some poison and will lie down with her in the tomb. Then he will kill himself. That way, they will be together. Forever!

Paris is approaching the family tomb to lay flowers on Juliet's grave, just as Romeo is riding into Verona.

Friar John has finally got back to Verona and has told Friar Laurence that he couldn't deliver the message to Romeo.

So Friar Laurence rushes to the Capulet tomb to try to sort it all out.

Everybody is trying to get to the spot where Juliet lies unmoving, deep in her death-like sleep.

It is all coming together as if it were meant to be. Just like in a good play!

First to meet are Paris and Romeo. Paris has never liked Romeo and he blames him for Juliet's death.

Paris thinks that Juliet died of grief over Tybalt's death. No way is he going to let Romeo, Tybalt's murderer, past.

For his part, Romeo is just mad with worry and has to see Juliet.

When Romeo finds Paris blocking his way, he tries to avoid violence. Romeo tells Paris:

'*Good gentle youth, tempt not a desperate man;*

Fly hence, and leave me ...

Put not another sin upon my head,

By urging me to fury.'

But Paris attacks him anyway, and Romeo catches him with a thrust of his sword.

Paris falls and dies. (Well, we can't say he wasn't warned!)

Paris' last wish is that Romeo place him with Juliet in the tomb:

'If thou be merciful,

Open the tomb, lay me with Juliet.'

So Romeo breaks into the tomb. At last he will see his Juliet!

With the tomb open, Romeo sees Juliet lying there. He is astonished by her beauty: she looks almost as if she is still alive!

'O my love! my wife!

Death … hath had no power yet upon thy beauty.'

Yet Death has taken everything. Tybalt lies there, dead. Paris lies there, dead.

Romeo takes Juliet in his arms. His tears fall on her poor, dead face. He wants to be with her forever.

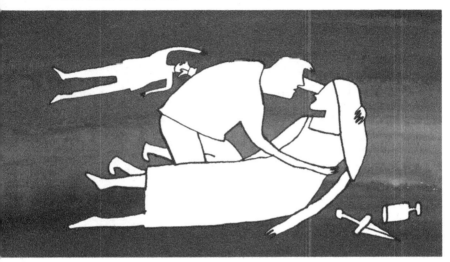

So Romeo gulps down the poison he carries with him and dies, kissing his love as he does so.

'*Thus with a kiss I die.*'

Just at that moment, Juliet wakes up and Friar Laurence rushes into the tomb. The friar takes in the scene in a glance and urges Juliet to come away.

But Juliet will not leave. So the friar departs, leaving Juliet at the tomb.

Juliet sees the poison in her lover's hand. She realises that he is dead.

If Romeo is dead, she decides that she must hurry to follow him, or she will lose control of her life again. She would face a life empty and grey without Romeo, shut up with some old nuns somewhere.

Quickly! Juliet kisses Romeo, trying to get some poison from his lips so that she may die. Her heart breaks as she realises that his lips are still warm. He has only just died.

So Juliet takes up Romeo's dagger and plunges it into her chest. She falls back dead.

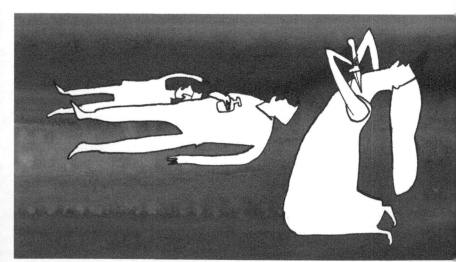

Now it seems as if the whole of Verona are crowding into the Capulet's tomb where the young people lie dead.

The friar has found his courage now (too late!), and he tells the whole story of the *'pair of star-cross'd lovers'*.

Too late the lords of both the Montagues and the Capulets realise that hatred is pointless and brings nothing but death.

They agree to end their family feuding. Prince Escales is particularly grateful for this new era of peace. He addresses the crowd:

'For never was a story of more woe
Than this of Juliet and her Romeo.'

 **THE END**

What's the play about?

More than anything else, this is a story of passion. The young lovers, Romeo and Juliet, try to be together, but it seems the world is against them. They are both very young, but they have to deal with hatred and feuding that is nothing to do with them.

Or was this how it was meant to be? Was it their fate?

This play is the world's most famous love story.

* It's about love – and about hate.

* It's about how teenagers become independent of their parents. (Getting married in secret has to be the ultimate teenage rebellion!)

*   It's about how fate – and love – works. (What if Rosaline and Romeo had become a couple and Romeo hadn't gone to the ball?)

*   It's about conflict, the feud between the two families – even though the reasons for the conflict have long been forgotten. The families fight because that's what they have always done.

*   It's about how people get tied up in other peoples' conflicts. (Mercutio and Paris both die, but neither of them are Capulets or Montagues.) Violence can spread.

*   It's about the tragic results feuds can bring, in general.

What are the main themes in the play?

Love – not just between Romeo & Juliet, but other kinds of love too: between friends and family.

Fate – or chance. Is this how it was meant to be, all along? Or did these people choose what happened to them?

Death – a lot of people die in this play, in different ways and for different reasons.

Honour – the feuding families, the reasons to fight (and die).

Opposites (or twos) – love and hate, war and peace, death and life, Montagues and Capulets.

Miscommunication – and what happens when something is misunderstood. If Romeo had got Friar Laurence's message, he wouldn't have killed himself. Also, a lot of Mercutio's wit is based on how words can have double meanings. Language is such a tricky thing.

These themes are universal. They are as important today as they were in Verona five hundred years ago. That is why the play is still popular today.

Shakespeare's words

Shakespeare loved to make up his own words and phrases. Many of them are now part of everyday English.

For example, '*wild-goose chase*' is from Shakespeare: it first appeared in this play. And we still call a 'ladies' man', or a womaniser, a bit of a '*Romeo*'.

Shakespeare uses language in this play in different ways and for different reasons.

Sometimes Shakespeare wants us to know what his characters are **thinking**.

* When Juliet is about to drink Friar Laurence's potion, in order to appear to be dead, we hear her tortured thoughts. (This kind of speech, that

nobody else is meant to hear, is called
a **soliloquy**.)

In this play Shakespeare uses many
metaphors and **similes** to paint vivid
pictures in our minds.

* When Romeo first sees Juliet at the
  window, he uses the metaphor of light:
  > '*But, soft! what light through yonder
  > window breaks?*
  > *It is the east, and Juliet is the sun.*
  > *Arise, fair sun, and kill the envious
  > moon.*'

  It is as if Juliet is a source of warmth
  and light to him.

Shakespeare also uses different kinds of
language for different characters in the
play.

Juliet's nurse is quite rough and bawdy,
and she uses quite crude language. When
she returns to Juliet after getting details of
the wedding arrangements, she complains

about her aching bones, but then points out that Juliet will be busy that night (with Romeo):

'You shall bear the burden soon at night.'

Friar Laurence, on the other hand, is more philosophical, less in touch with such earthy matters. His language seems to be full of words of wisdom. For example, after Romeo and Juliet are married, he says:

'These violent delights have violent ends.'

The way Shakespeare chooses the language that different characters use helps us understand their personalties.